Published by Melanin Origins LLC
PO Box 122123; Arlington, TX 76012

First Edition

Library of Congress Control Number: 2017919489

ISBN: 9781626768185 hardback
ISBN: 9781626768109 paperback
ISBN: 9781626768178 ebook

Dedication

This book is dedicated to my sons: Taylor and Aaron Payton. You two have supported and encouraged me throughout my journey and service in the Armed Forces. Furthermore, I dedicate this work of art to all children who have parents that proudly serve in the military. You are a symbol of hope and a beacon of light to your parents. Let the adventure begin!

Aloha! My name is Taylor and these are my STEM adventures. STEM stands for Science, Technology, Engineering and Math.

My mom and dad are both in the U.S. Army. My mom is a Chemical Officer and my dad is an Engineer Officer. I get my love for science from my mom and I like building things just like my dad.

Because of their jobs we have the chance to live and visit exciting places. My parent's current jobs are in Honolulu, Hawaii.

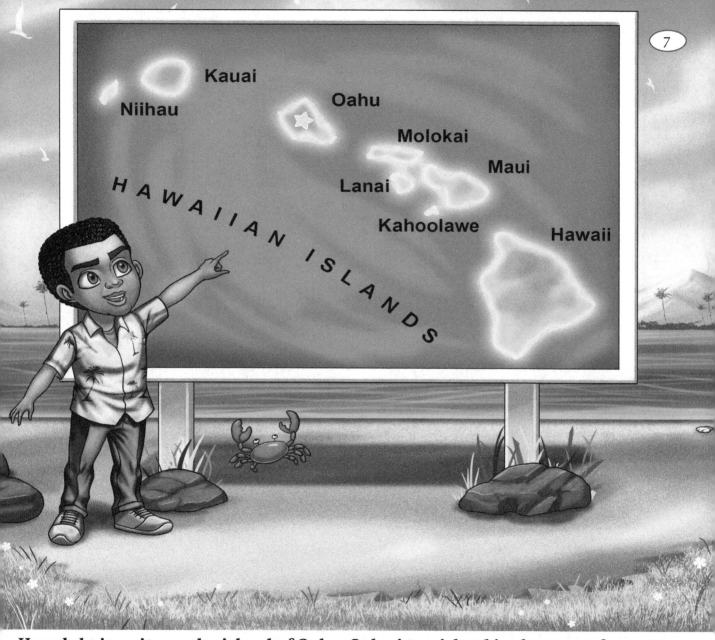

Honolulu is a city on the island of Oahu. Oahu is an island in the state of Hawaii. The state of Hawaii is made up of eight islands. They include Hawaii, Maui, Oahu, Kahoolawe, Lanai, Molokai, Kauai and Niihau. There is also the island of Kaala which is small like me and sometimes overlooked.

The Hawaiian Islands were created by the movement of tectonic plates over hot spots in the earth. This caused volcanoes to form. The lava from the volcanoes was cooled by the water and this created the islands.

My parents took me to see Kilauea, an active volcano at the Hawaii Volcano National Park. While there, we walked down into the lava tubes which are caves that are made when magma reaches Earth's surface. The caves were very dark so we had to use flash lights to see.

The best part of the trip was when we went to see Kilauea at night. Night time is the best time to see the red hot lava erupting from the volcano and falling into the ocean.

When we returned home my mom told me that Waianae and Koolau are the two volcano's that created the island of Oahu where we live. But they are both inactive right now.

The most popular landmark created by the Koolau volcano is Diamond Head in Waikiki. One day, my parents and I hiked all the way to the top of Diamond Head which is 1.3 kilometers long or a little less than one mile. We could see all of Waikiki and some other islands.

In school, we learned that Volcanologists are the scientist that study volcanos. Several Volcanologists have visited our class.

Have you ever gone swimming at the beach on Christmas day? I have! Because Hawaii is near the equator it is warm most of the time. At sea level temperatures rarely rise above 90°F or drop below 60°F. It often snows in Hawaii's high altitudes like the mountains in the winter.

Did you know about 71% of the earth is covered by water and 96% of that water is in the oceans? Many scientists come to Hawaii to study the island's different ecosystems. My favorite scientist is an Oceanographer who studies marine biology. Marine biologists study the plants and animals living in a marine environment.

In Hawaii you can see marine plants like sea grasses, seaweed and algae. There are many marine animals in Hawaii too. You can find reef fish, sea turtles, humpback whales and bottlenose dolphins. You can also find the Hawaiian Monk seal which is a seal that is native only to the Hawaiian Islands.

I like snorkeling so I can see marine animals in their habitat. One day I touched a starfish it was hard and bumpy.

I went on a submarine adventure with mom and dad, and we could see marine life up close. We saw coral, tropical fish, turtles and sharks.

In school my teacher built an underwater robot controlled by her computer. The robot took underwater pictures, and she shared them in class with us.

Hawaii is not only a great place to study things underwater, it is also a great place to study the skies. Hawaii's observatories help astronomers study the vast outer space.

There are many observatories in Hawaii, but the Mauna Kea Observatory is one of the largest in the world. Astronomers from eleven countries operate its 13 telescopes.

Hawaiian observatories are located high above sea level and it snows at many of them. Mauna Kea Observatory is more than 13,000 feet above sea level and sometimes gets enough snow to ski or snowboard.

What are the colors of the Rainbow? The colors are red, orange, yellow, green, blue, indigo and violet. The teacher taught us the acronym ROY G. BIV to help us remember them.

Because of the rain and mist in the Hawaiian air, rainbows are seen everywhere. So Hawaii has been nicknamed "The Rainbow State".

Rainbows are made when sunlight is separated by a raindrop. Sunlight is made up of colors and the rain acts like a prism to divide each color.

Oahu
Marine Corps: Kaneohe Bay, Camp Smith
Army: Fort Shafter, Schofield Barracks, Tripler AMC
Navy: Joint Base Pearl Harbor-Hickam, NCTAMS PAC
Air Force: Joint Base Pearl Harbor-Hickam, Bellows Air Force Station
Coast Guard: USCG ISC Honolulu, Barbers Point

In Hawaii there are many military instillations. My mom works at Camp Smith, a Marine Corps base. My dad works at Joint Base Pearl Harbor-Hickam, a combined Air Force and Navy base.

Two of my favorite military places in Hawaii are Tripler Medical Center and the USS Arizona Memorial.

Tripler Medical Center is a big pink hospital in the Moanalua area near my school. The architect was inspired to use the coral pink color from the nearby Royal Hawaiian Hotel. Dad told me the architect also borrowed other design features from the hotel during its construction.

The USS Arizona Memorial is one of the Pearl Harbor's historical sites. Other sites include the Battleship Missouri Memorial, the USS Bowfin Submarine Museum and the Pacific Aviation Museum.

The USS Arizona Memorial is built over the USS Arizona sunken battleship and is 184 feet long with 21 windows. The windows represent an ongoing 21 gun salute to the battleships' crew.

Mom, Dad and I will be in Hawaii for two more years. We still have lots to see and do on the islands of Hawaii, and after that we will be on to our next adventure! I cannot wait to see where the military will take us next and the STEM adventures we will have in the future. See you soon, but for now, Aloha from Taylor!

Vocabulary Part 1

Air - The atmosphere that surrounds the earth.

Aloha –A word used in greeting and farewells, and expressing love.

Animals - Any of a kingdom of living things including many-celled organisms and often many of the single-celled ones that typically differ from plants.

Architect - A person who designs buildings and advises in their construction.

Astronomer –A scientific observer of the celestial bodies and the Universe as a whole.

Astronomy – Is the study of the Universe and the changes that take place in and around all objects moving through space.

Coral – Corals are sea animals that stay in one place throughout their adult lives.

Ecosystem - All the living and nonliving things in an environment and all their interactions.

Environment - The things, both living and nonliving, that surround a living thing.

Equator – The imaginary east-west line encircling the Earth midway between the North and South poles.

Vocabulary Part 2

Habitat - The natural home or environment of an animal, plant, or other organism

Hot spots –A volcanic hotspot is where lava pushes up from under the mantle and creates a volcano.

Island – A piece of land surrounded by water.

Lava – Is magma that flows onto the Earth's surface.

Observatory – A facility for observing or monitoring environmental conditions or phenomena on Earth or in space.

Prism - optical device having a triangular shape and made of glass or quartz; used to deviate a beam or invert an image.

Rain - Water that returns to Earth as precipitation after it becomes vapor and cools to again form water.

Rainbow - A rainbow is a multicolored arc, or curved line, in the sky.

Plate Tectonics – Earth's surface is divided into plates that move over the mantle

Volcano – A mountain that forms when red-hot melted rock flows through a crack onto Earth's surface.

CPSIA information can be obtained
at www.ICGtesting.com
Printed in the USA
LVHW060149020819
626092LV00007B/2/P